Somewhere in the Ocean

Somewhere in the Ocean

by *Jennifer Ward* and T. J. Marsh

illustrated by Kenneth J. Spengler

SCHOLASTIC INC.
New York Toronto London Auckland Sydney
Mexico City New Delhi Hong Kong

The illustrations were rendered in gouache on watercolor paper.
The text type was set in Poppi-Laudito
The display type was set in Phaistos
Designed by Michael Russell
Edited by Aimee Jackson

ISBN 0-439-22035-1

12 11 10 9 8 7 6 5 4   6 7 8/0

Printed in the U.S.A.   40

First Scholastic printing, January 2001

For all children curious about the wonders beneath the waves.

— J. W.

For my parents, Lora and Russ Hileman, for believing in me long before I believed in myself.

— T. J. M.

To Margaret, Matthew, Mom, and Dad, for all the fun we've had at the shore.

— K. S.

Hey, kids!
Look for the number
hidden on each page!

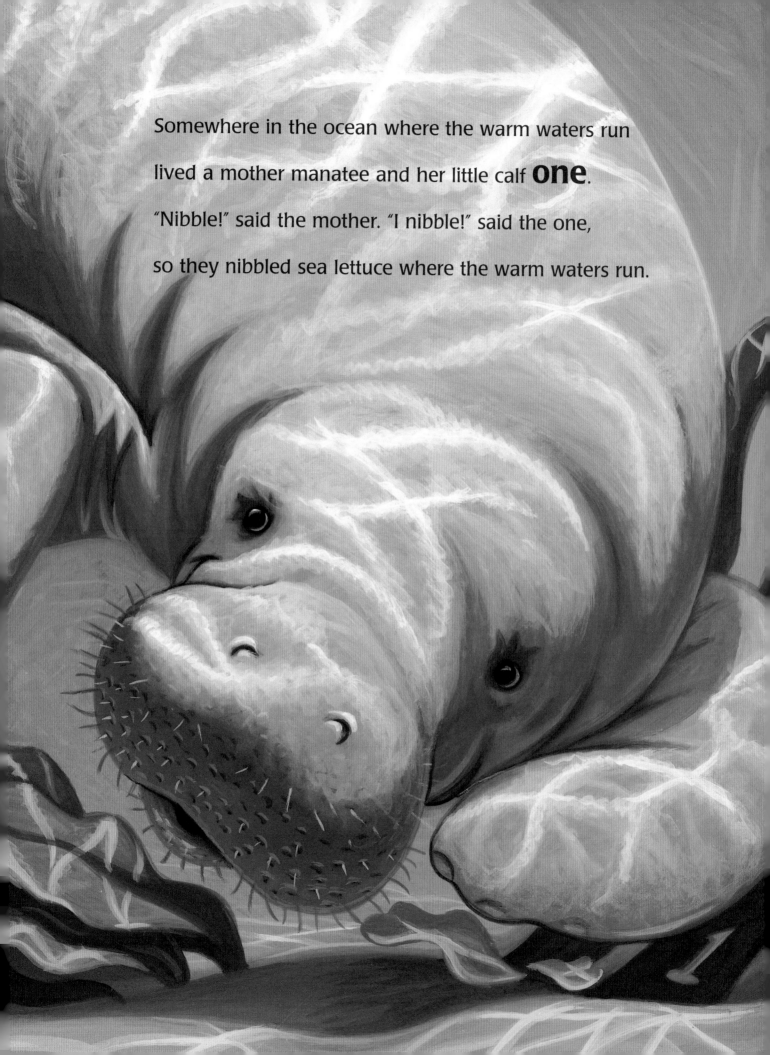

Somewhere in the ocean where the warm waters run

lived a mother manatee and her little calf **one**.

"Nibble!" said the mother. "I nibble!" said the one,

so they nibbled sea lettuce where the warm waters run.

Somewhere in the ocean in the waters clear and blue

lived a pod of orca whales and their little calves **two**.

"Splash!" said the mothers. "We splash!" said the two,

so they jumped and they splashed in the waters clear and blue.

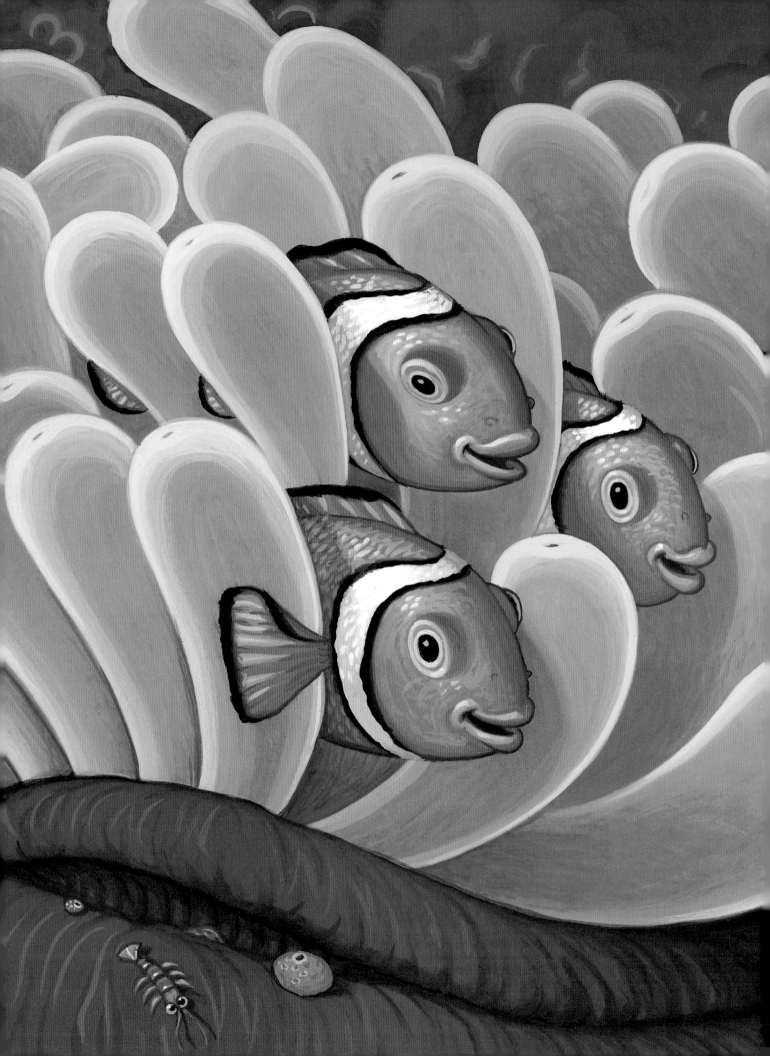

Somewhere in the ocean in a sea anemone

lived a mother clown fish and her baby fish **three**.

"Nestle!" said the mother. "We nestle!" said the three,

so they nestled safe and snug in their sea anemone.

Somewhere in the ocean in a tide pool by the shore

lived a mother hermit crab and her baby crabs **four**.

"Dress!" said the mother. "We dress!" said the four,

so they tried on different shells in their tide pool by the shore.

Somewhere in the ocean where the kelp forests thrive

lived a raft of sea otters and their baby otters **five**.

"Munch!" said the mothers. "We munch!" said the five,

so they munched prickly urchins where the kelp forests thrive.

Somewhere in the ocean where the seas and rivers mix

lived a mother tiger shark and her little pups **six**.

"Cruise!" said the mother. "We cruise!" said the six,

so they cruised and they hunted where the seas and rivers mix.

Somewhere in the ocean where the sea grass grows so even

lived a father sea horse and his wee babies **seven**.

"Hold on!" said the father. "We hold on!" said the seven,

so they held and they swayed where the sea grass grows so even.

Somewhere in the ocean where the water shimmers late

lived a mother sea turtle and her baby turtles **eight**.

"Paddle!" said the mother. "We paddle!" said the eight,

so they paddled in the moonlight where the water shimmers late.

Somewhere in the ocean drifting slowly in a line

lived a mother jellyfish and her baby jellies **nine**.

"Zap!" said the mother. "We zap!" said the nine,

so they zapped tasty tidbits as they drifted in a line.

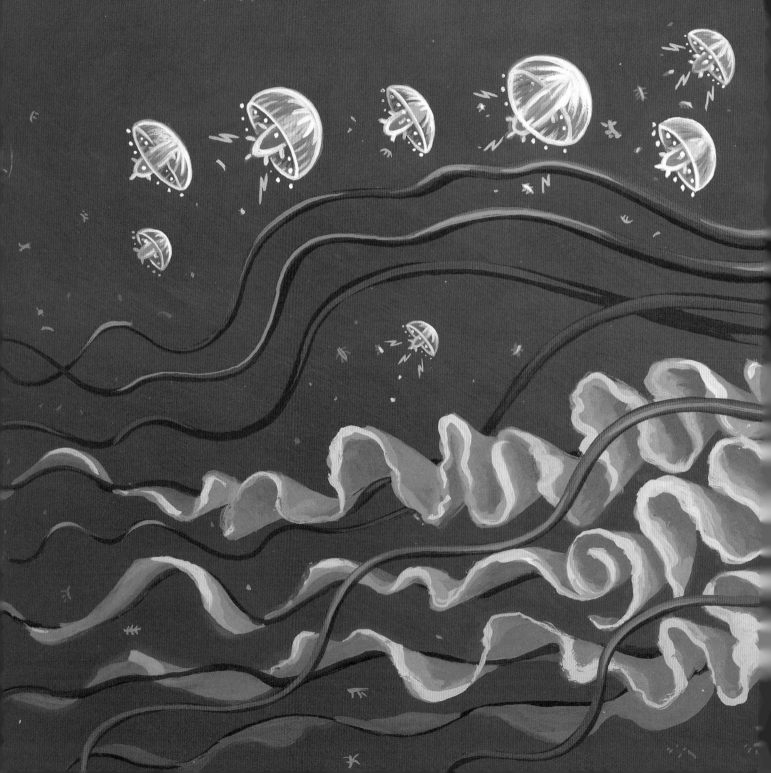

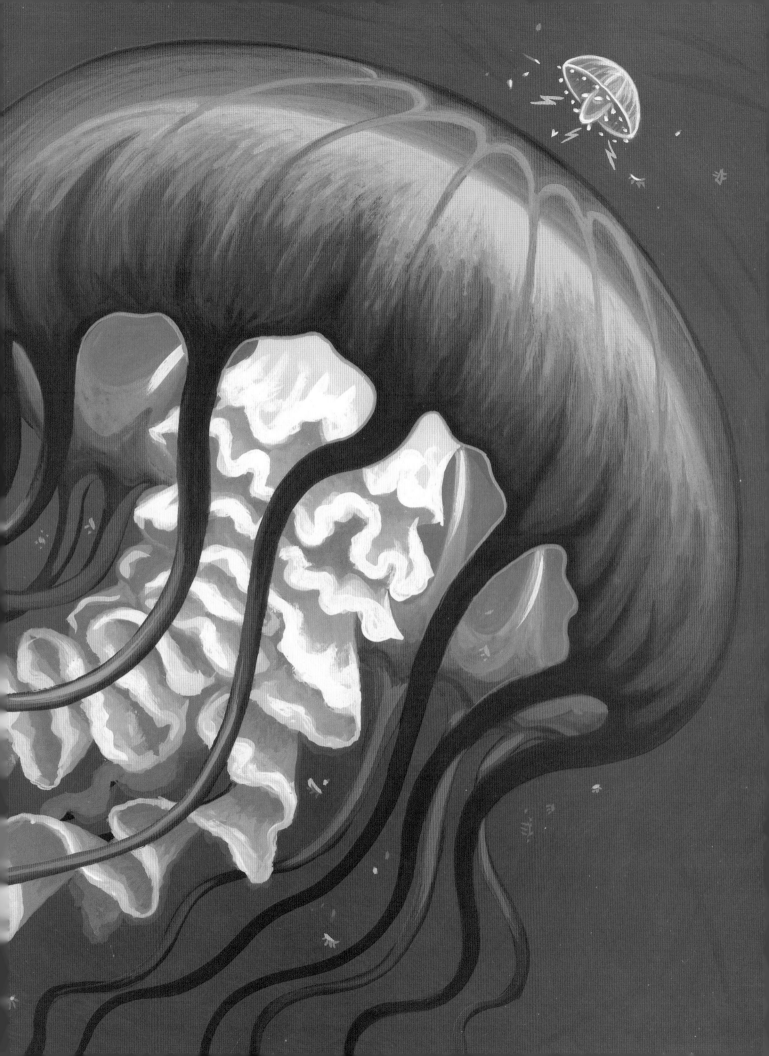

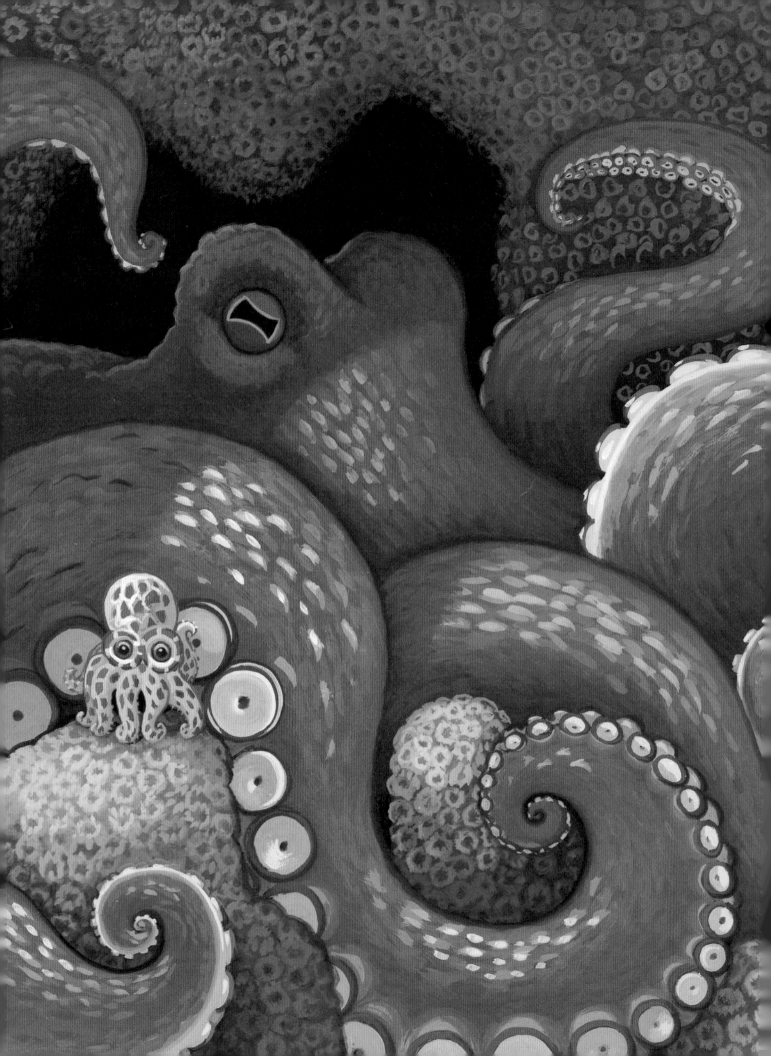

Somewhere in the ocean in a coral reef den

lived a mother octopus and her little babies **ten**.

"Squirt!" said the mother. "We squirt!" said the ten,

so they squirted and they played in their coral reef den.

Fun Facts

 **clown fish**—This colorful fish is also known as the clown anemone fish because it spends most of its time swimming among the stinging tentacles of sea anemones. For many other fish, swimming near an anemone would be harmful or deadly. But not to the clown anemone fish! When in danger, it may even swim all the way inside the anemone's mouth! Seeking shelter within the anemone helps protect the clown anemone fish from predators. Clown anemone fish live in the coral reefs of the Atlantic and Pacific oceans.

coral reef—People often mistake coral for a plant, but it is actually made up of tiny animals called polyps. Polyps don't grow into one large animal like we do. Instead, they grow by making lots and lots of little copies of themselves. They may attach themselves to a rock, shell, or even a crab. As the group of polyps becomes larger, it is called a coral colony. The coral colony begins to take on a special shape as it grows. Some might look like lumpy rocks, while others might look like branches, antlers, or fans. Many different coral colonies growing near one another form a beautiful and colorful coral reef that looks like a fantastic underwater garden!

 **hermit crab**—Unlike most crabs, hermit crabs do not grow shells of their own. They must use an empty shell from another animal as their home in order to protect their soft bodies. As the hermit crab grows, it must move from its "borrowed" home into a larger one! Hermit crabs live in the coastal waters of the Atlantic and Pacific oceans.

invertebrate—Every animal on the planet either has a backbone or does not have a backbone. Animals that do not have backbones are called invertebrates. Can you find the invertebrate animals in this book?

jellyfish—Jellyfish do not swim very well. As they drift with the current, their tentacles collide with small fish and shrimp that are swimming by or that are also being swept along with the current. When this happens, the tentacles zap and stun the animal unfortunate enough to collide with those stinging tentacles. Then the jellyfish draws the prey up into its mouth at the center of its body, and it's lunch time for the jellyfish! Jellyfish can be found in oceans all over the world.

kelp forest—The kelp forest is a very special underwater forest, home to many ocean animals. It is made up of very long strands of kelp, which is a type of underwater plant. Attached to the sea floor, the kelp grows upward toward the surface, sometimes taller than a ten-story building! Sea otters help keep kelp forests healthy by eating prickly sea urchins that can be damaging to the kelp.

manatee—Manatees are mammals, just like whales, dolphins, and you! They spend their entire lives in water, but like all mammals, they must go to the surface to breathe. Can you believe that a long time ago, sailors mistook cute, chubby, gray manatees for beautiful mermaids? These gentle, slow moving creatures live in shallow warm waters where they graze on sea grasses, water weeds, and algae. These animals are about as long and as heavy as a small car. To get that way, they must eat one pound of food for every ten pounds of body weight. That would be like you eating about five or six pounds of salad every day! Manatees live in the coastal waters of the Gulf of Mexico and the Caribbean, and in some of the warm rivers that feed into them. They are also found in the rivers of tropical Africa.

octopus—Octopuses are some of the most intelligent animals in the ocean. They can get to food that is inside a jar with the lid screwed on! One of the special things about them is that not only can they change the color of their skin, but they can also change the texture of it to blend in with their surroundings. They can look like a piece of seaweed or a bit of coral if they choose to! This is called posturing. Sometimes different colors mean different things to an octopus. When they turn white, it usually means they are frightened, while red means they are angry. An octopus can also squirt dark-colored ink into the water, which is used to confuse predators so the octopus can escape undetected. An octopus mother dies shortly after her eggs hatch. Octopuses can be found in oceans all over the world.

orca—Also known as the killer whale, the orca is actually the largest member of the dolphin family! Its "killer" nickname was given because orcas have been known to eat other whales, as well as seals, sea lions, fish, and walrus. They never eat people, though. Once an orca almost ate a surfer, but spit him out when it realized its mistake! Orcas have only one baby at a time called a calf. The calf drinks its mother's milk, just like a human baby. They can live as long as people and stay in the same pod with their mothers for most of their lives. Orcas can be found in oceans all over the world.

pod—A pod is the name given to a group of animals that live and stay together as a very large family. There are many advantages to living in a pod. For example, animals that live within a pod may help one another with caring for their young, hunting, and may even play with one another! Most whales, dolphins, and seals are known to live in pods.

sea anemone—Sea anemones look like colorful underwater flowers, but they are actually animals! Their many long, leaf-like tentacles are capable of stinging and are used by the anemones to stun and catch their prey.

sea horse—Sea horses are fish, but they do not swim very well, so they tend to spend most of their time with their tails wrapped tightly around sea grass or seaweed to keep them anchored. The father sea horse is responsible for hatching the young. The mother deposits her eggs into the father's pouch, similar to the pouch of a kangaroo. The eggs are then protected within the pouch for a few weeks, and when they're ready, the father delivers the newborn sea horses! Sea horses live in the shallow, grassy waters of oceans worldwide.

sea otter—The sea otter is a mammal that spends a lot of its time in the ocean. A mother has only one pup at a time, and even it is born out at sea. They spend much of their time in the kelp forests where they dive for clams, sea urchins, abalone, and octopuses. When they get a clam or other animal inside a shell, they float on their backs and break their dinner open with a rock they brought up from the bottom. When napping, they grab some kelp and roll over until they are all wrapped up. That way they won't float away! Sea otters live along some coastal waters of the Pacific ocean.

sea turtle—Some sea turtles grow to be really big, bigger than a really big man. As soon as they hatch in a nest on a sandy beach, they scramble for the water, trying to avoid crabs, sea birds, and other animals that would like nothing better than to have a baby sea turtle for lunch. They live by themselves and swim all over the ocean for about twenty years. Then they return to the very beach where they were hatched, and the females crawl up onto the beach. Then they dig a hole in the sand and lay their eggs. The cycle starts all over again. Sea turtles live in the Atlantic, Pacific, and Indian oceans.

sea urchin—Sea urchins are round-shaped, spiny ocean animals that use tiny, tube-like feet to move around the ocean and grab their food. Even with all those little spikes for protection, the sea urchin is still considered tasty by many ocean animals. Many people think that sea urchins are delicious, too, but the authors are not among them!

tide pool—Tide pools are created near rocky shorelines. As the tide lowers and goes out to sea, it leaves behind little pools of calm water trapped in the rocky crevices called tide pools. Tide pools are wonderful places to explore a sampling of ocean life! You may find sea urchins, anemones, crabs, and even fish! But tide pools are an important habitat for many animals, and they can be easily damaged. If you have the opportunity to visit a tide pool, be sure to explore kindly and carefully. And never take the plants or animals you find home with you.

tiger shark—Tiger sharks can grow to be eighteen feet long—that's about three times longer than a grown man is tall. These animals eat everything, and they are always hungry! They have been known to eat fish, other sharks, turtles, dolphins, tin cans, garbage, and even people. You can see why they don't make good pets! Tiger sharks can be found in oceans all over the world.

vertebrate—This is the word scientists use to talk about animals with a backbone. Lots of animals have backbones. Dogs and cats have backbones. Even you have a backbone. Can you find all the animals in this book that have backbones?

Somewhere in the Ocean

Some - where   in   the   o - cean   where   the   warm wat - ers

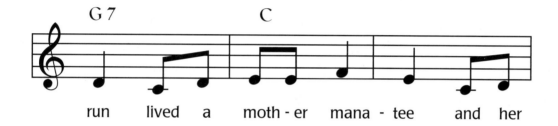

run   lived   a   moth - er   mana - tee   and   her

lit - tle   calf   one.   "Nibb - le!" said   the   moth - er.   "I

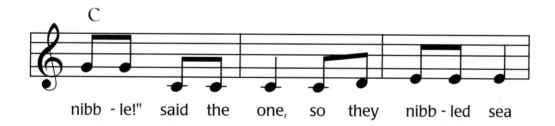

nibb - le!"   said   the   one,   so   they   nibb - led   sea

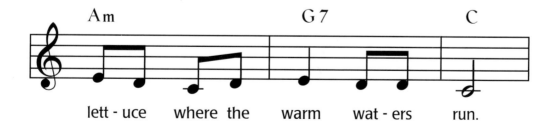

lett - uce   where   the   warm   wat - ers   run.

Jennifer Ward and her family escape to the beaches neighboring their home in Arizona as often as their schedules allow, where they (kindly and carefully) explore tide pools and relish the wonders and magic of the sea. Jennifer lives in Tucson with her husband, Richard, and their daughter, Kelly.

T. J. Marsh has been scuba diving with sharks and lion fish in Fiji, with moray eels in the Caribbean, with seals off the coast of California, and with manatees in the Florida Keys. T. J. lives in Tucson, Arizona, with her husband, Phil, and their daughters, Riley and Tiernay.

Kenneth J. Spengler began his career as an illustrator shortly after he graduated from Tyler School of Art with a B. F. A. His work can be found on anything from posters to billboards, and from mystery covers to children's books such as *Way Out in the Desert* and *A Campfire for Cowboy Billy*.